Miss Seager.

G000293257

PHONICS

with **Marty Monkey**

Stage 3

AGES 4-7

Contents

a a a a a a a a a a a a a a a a a a a a a a a

Join the letters to make the word.

Read the word. Hear the letter sounds.

h **a** t

hat

Join the letters to make the words.

m **a** t   c **a** t   r **a** t

_____   _____   _____

Label the pictures correctly.

_____   _____   _____

Join the letters to make the words and write them below. Draw a picture of the word.

_____   _____   _____

v **a** n   p **a** n   f **a** n

PARENT'S TIPS   Say the sound of each letter in each word several times (eg huh ah tuh) and gradually speed up until the sounds run together.

Use the words in the box below to do the crosswords.

bag	tap	van	jam
ram	wag	cap	fan

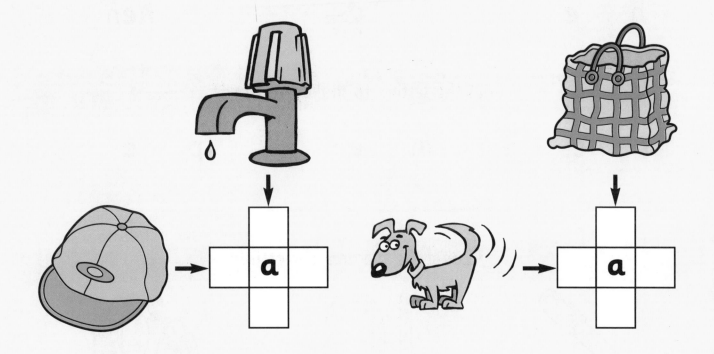

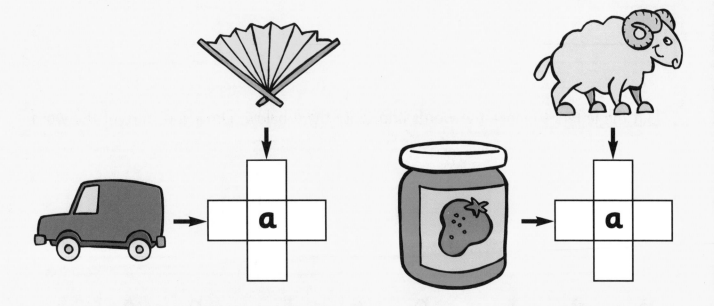

PARENT'S TIPS — Name each picture one at a time and find the word in the box before helping your child write it in the correct place in each crossword.

3

e e e e e e e e e e e e e e e e e e e e e e e e

Join the letters to make the word.

Read the word. Hear the letter sounds.

h e n

hen

Join the letters to make the words.

t e n   m e n   p e n

_____   _____   _____

Label the pictures correctly.

10

_____   _____   _____

Join the letters to make the words and write them below. Draw a picture of the word.

w e t   p e t   n e t

4

PARENT'S TIPS

Say the sound of each letter in each word several times (eg huh eh nuh) and gradually speed up until the sounds run together.

e e e e e e e e e e e e e e e e e e e e e e e

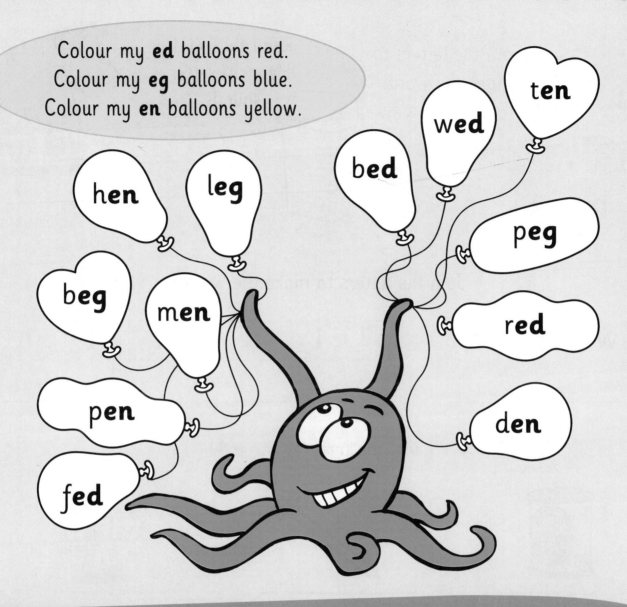

Colour my **ed** balloons red.
Colour my **eg** balloons blue.
Colour my **en** balloons yellow.

Sort the words in the balloons into sets and write them in the boxes below.

ed words	**eg** words	**en** words

PARENT'S
TIPS

After colouring all the balloons and writing the words in
sets, see how many other rhyming words you can think of.

5

Join the letters to make the word.

Read the word. Hear the letter sounds.

b i n

bin

Join the letters to make the words.

w i n   p i n   t i n

_____   _____   _____

Label the pictures correctly.

_____   _____   _____

Join the letters to make the words and write them below. Draw a picture of the word.

s i x   m i x   f i x

PARENT'S TIPS Say the sound of each letter in each word several times (eg buh ih nuh) and gradually speed up until the sounds run together.

Join the rhyming words.

Write the rhyming words.

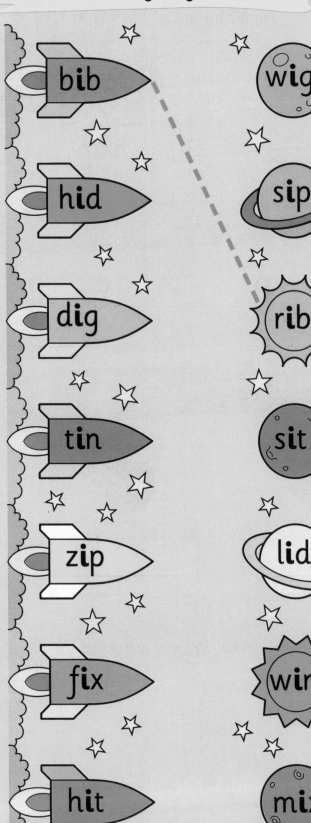

bib   rib

Join the letters to make the word.

Read the word. Hear the letter sounds.

h o p

h**o**p

Join the letters to make the words.

p o p   t o p   m o p

_____   _____   _____

Label the pictures correctly.

Join the letters to make the words and write them below. Draw a picture of the word.

d o g   f o g   l o g

PARENT'S TIPS

Say the sound of each letter in each word several times (eg huh oh puh) and gradually speed up until the sounds run together.

Write in the missing **o** to finish the words.

c __ t   s __ b   f __ x

_____   _____   _____

b __ x   p __ t   r __ b

_____   _____   _____

Write the missing letters. Write the words below.

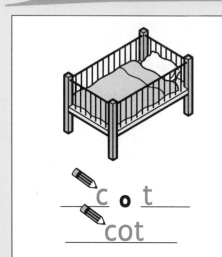

c o t

cot

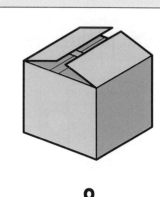

__ o __

_____

__ o __

_____

__ __ o

_____

__ o __

_____

__ o __

_____

PARENT'S TIPS After making up the words on the top half of the page, ask your child to name each picture before trying to find the word that goes with it.

9

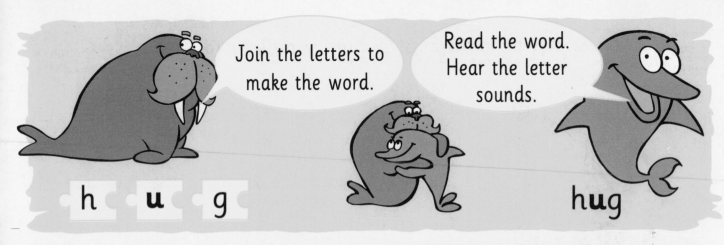

Join the letters to make the word.

Read the word. Hear the letter sounds.

h **u** g

h**u**g

Join the letters to make the words.

m **u** g   j **u** g   r **u** g

_____   _____   _____

Label the pictures correctly.

Join the letters to make the words and write them below. Draw a picture of the word.

r **u** n   s **u** n   b **u** n

PARENT'S TIPS Say the sound of each letter in each word several times (eg huh uh guh) and gradually speed up until the sounds run together.

- Play this game with a partner.
- You need two counters and a coin.
- Take it in turns to spin the coin.
  Tails = move one space. Heads = move two spaces.
- If you can't read the word you land on, miss a turn.
- The first person to hop across the pond is the winner.

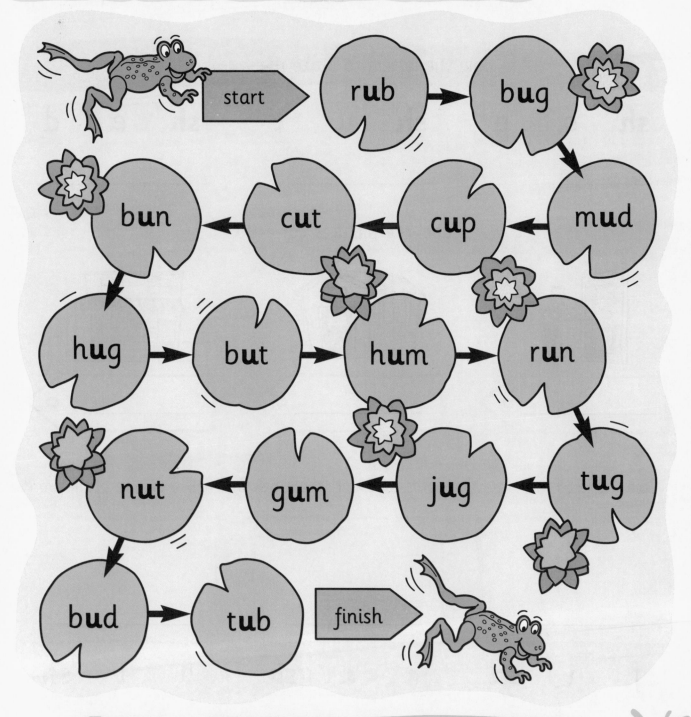

start → rub → bug → mud → cup → cut → bun → hug → but → hum → run → tug → jug → gum → nut → bud → tub → finish

PARENT'S TIPS If your child has difficulty with any of the words, point to each letter one at a time, say its sound and help your child 'build up' the word.

11

Join the letters to make the word.

Read the word. Hear the letter sounds.

sh **i** **p**

ship

Join the letters to make the words.

sh **o** **p**

sh **u** **t**

sh **e** **d**

_____

_____

_____

Label the pictures correctly.

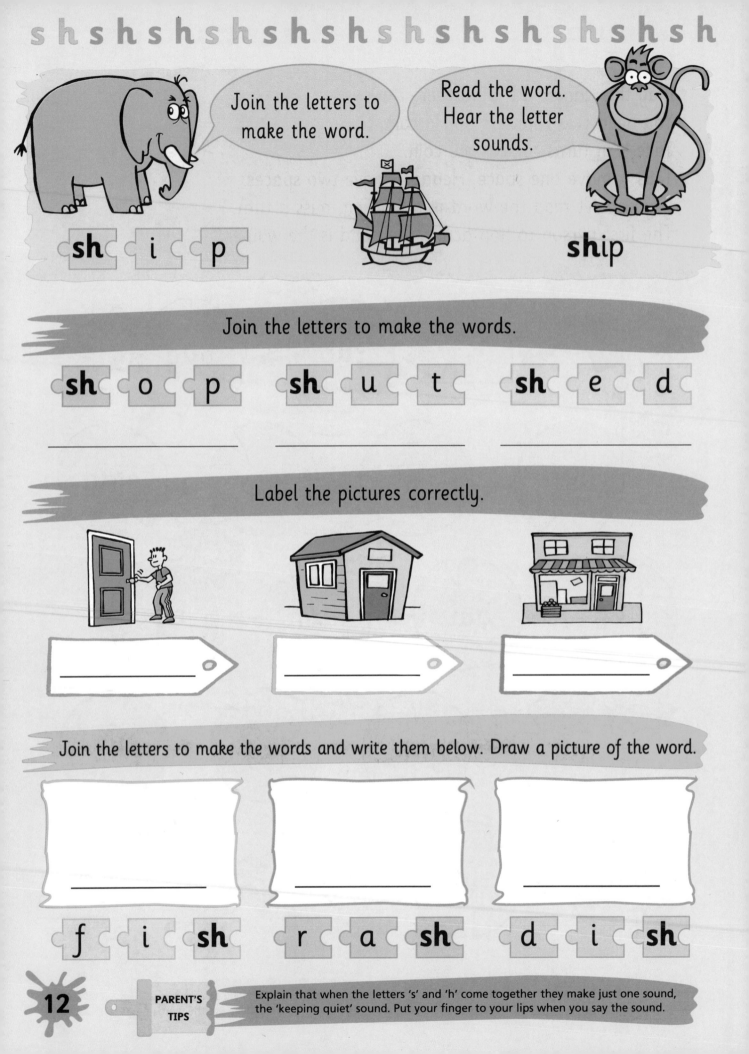

_____

_____

_____

Join the letters to make the words and write them below. Draw a picture of the word.

_____

_____

_____

f **i** **sh**

r **a** **sh**

d **i** **sh**

PARENT'S TIPS Explain that when the letters 's' and 'h' come together they make just one sound, the 'keeping quiet' sound. Put your finger to your lips when you say the sound.

Label the things on each **sh**elf that contain **sh**.

shell

shark

ship

shoe

sheep

bru**sh**

bu**sh**

fi**sh**

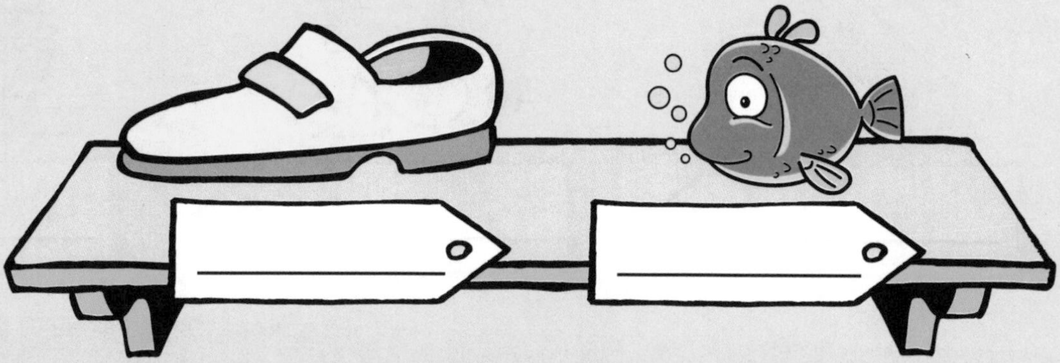

PARENT'S TIPS — Ask your child to name each thing on the shelves, before trying to find the word that goes with it.

Join the letters to make the word.

Read the word. Hear the letter sounds.

ch a t

chat

Join the letters to make the words.

ch i n   ch o p   ch i p

_____   _____   _____

Label the pictures correctly.

_____   _____   _____

Join the letters to make the words and write them below. Draw a picture of the word.

_____   _____   _____

l u n **ch**   b u n **ch**   p u n **ch**

14

PARENT'S TIPS   Explain that when the letters 'c' and 'h' come together they make just one sound. Help your child to remember it by pretending to be a steam train and making chugging noises.

Use the words in the box below to do the crossword puzzle.

chips   **ch**est   **ch**imp   **ch**icken

tor**ch**   pin**ch**   ben**ch**

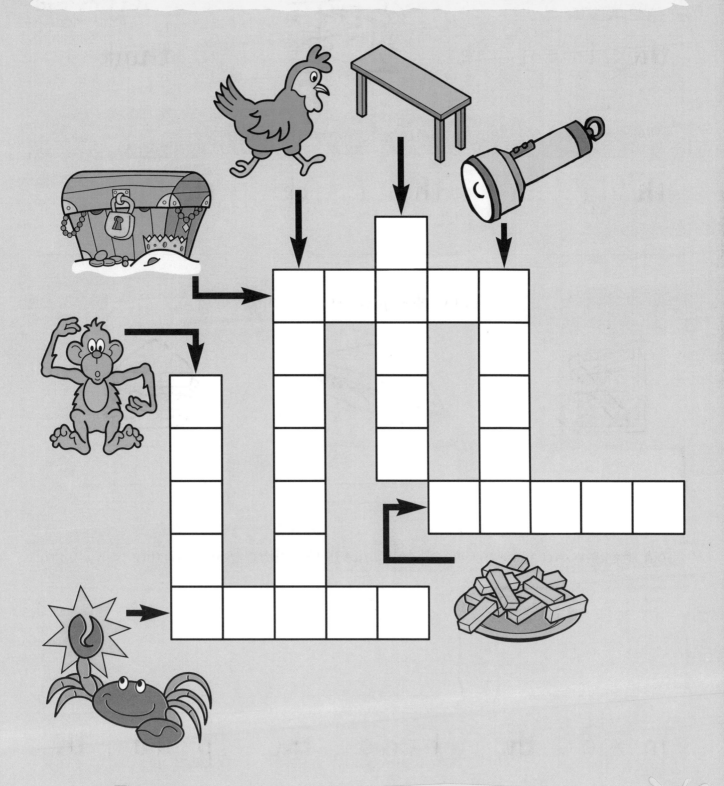

PARENT'S TIPS   Name each picture one at a time and find the word in the box, before helping your child write it in the correct place in the crossword.

15

Join the letters to make the word.

Read the word. Hear the letter sounds.

th i n k

think

Join the letters to make the words.

th i n   **th** i ck   **th** ie f

_____   _____   _____

Label the pictures correctly.

_____   _____   _____

Join the letters to make the words and write them below. Draw a picture of the word.

m o **th**   b a **th**   p a **th**

16

PARENT'S TIPS

Explain that when the letters 't' and 'h' come together they make just one sound. Tell your child it is the 'rude' sound because you have to put out your tongue to make it!

Find the **th** words in the bricks.

a b t h i n c d

t h i c k f g h

j k l t h a n k

m t h u m p r s

b a t h v w x y

z a b c p a t h

d f m o t h g i

j c l o t h k n

Write the words.

✏️ thin

_____

_____

_____

_____

_____

_____

_____

Sort the words in the bricks into sets and write them in the boxes below.

Words beginning with **th**

Words ending with **th**

PARENT'S TIPS Ask your child to be a 'word detective' and look for the 'th' words 'hiding' on the page. Developing a good eye for words is an important element of reading and spelling.

17

Join the letters to make the word.

Read the word. Hear the letter sounds.

h | i | ll

hill

Join the letters to make the words.

m | i | ll   t | i | ll   f | i | ll

_____   _____   _____

Label the pictures correctly.

_____   _____   _____

Join the letters to make the words and write them below. Draw a picture of the word.

_____   _____   _____

b | a | ll   f | a | ll   w | a | ll

PARENT'S TIPS When 'l' comes at the end of a short word it is always doubled – but it still makes the 'luh' sound.

Build the words.

Write the words.

| b |
| s |
| t |
| w |
| y |
| sh |

ell

✎ bell
_____
_____
_____
_____
_____

Use the words you made to write the answers.

1 You ring this.

2 A snail has one.

3 When you shout.

4 You can get water from this.

5 Shopkeepers do this.

6 You do this with a story.

✎ bell
_____
_____
_____
_____
_____

PARENT'S TIPS After making the words at the top of the page, get your child to read them aloud and notice they all rhyme. The ability to hear rhymes is very important in reading and spelling.

19

Join the letters to make the word.

Read the word. Hear the letter sounds.

l   i   ck

lick

Join the letters to make the words.

k   i   ck   t   i   ck   s   i   ck

_____   _____   _____

Label the pictures correctly.

_____   _____   _____

Join the letters to make the words and write them below. Draw a picture of the word.

_____   _____   _____

l   o   ck   r   o   ck   s   o   ck

20

PARENT'S
TIPS

We cannot use 'c' at the end of a short word.
The sound is always represented by the 'ck' letters.

Make as many **ack** and **uck** words as possible.
Use the letters in the bricks to begin your words.

Put the **ack** words in the sack.

Put the **uck** words in the duck.

l

m

b

sh

p

r

cl

s

tr

PARENT'S TIPS   Encourage your child to build up the words on this page in 'chunks' e.g. 'b' (buh) + 'ack' makes 'back'.

Join the letters to make the word.

Read the word. Hear the letter sounds.

k   i   ng

king

Join the letters to make the words.

r   i   ng   s   i   ng   w   i   ng

_____   _____   _____

Label the pictures correctly.

_____   _____   _____

Join the letters to make the words and write them below. Draw a picture of the word.

_____   _____   _____

b   a   ng   h   a   ng   g   a   ng

22

PARENT'S TIPS

Say the word 'king' and get your child to listen carefully to the end of it. Point out that the letters 'n' and 'g' make one sound when they come together.

Write the words under the correct pictures.

a si**ng**i**ng** thi**ng**

a swi**ng**i**ng** thi**ng**

a cli**ng**i**ng** thi**ng**

a sti**ng**i**ng** thi**ng**

a swinging thing

PARENT'S TIPS

Talk about the pictures with your child and work out which caption should go with each.

23

Join the letters to make the word.

Read the word. Hear the letter sounds.

c l a p

clap

Join the letters to make the words.

c l o ck   **p l** u g   **b l** o t

_____   _____   _____

Label the pictures correctly.

Join the letters to make the words and write them below. Draw a picture of the word.

f l a g   **s l** i p   **g l** a ss

24

PARENT'S TIPS

Encourage your child to say each sound and 'build up' each word by merging the sounds together.

- Play this game with a partner.
- You need two counters and a coin.
- Take it in turns to spin the coin.
  Tails = move one space. Heads = move two spaces.
- If you can't read the word you land on, miss a turn.
- The first person to reach the end is the winner.

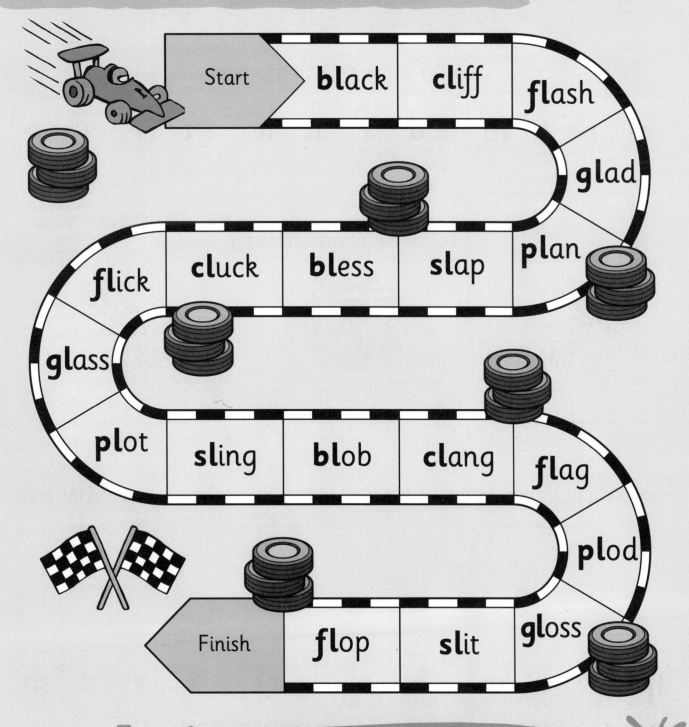

Start **bl**ack **cl**iff **fl**ash **gl**ad **pl**an

flick **cl**uck **bl**ess **sl**ap

glass

plot **sl**ing **bl**ob **cl**ang **fl**ag **pl**od **gl**oss

Finish **fl**op **sl**it

PARENT'S TIPS If your child has difficulty with any of the words, help your child to break the word up into smaller parts using the letter sounds.

25

Join the letters to make the word.

Read the word. Hear the letter sounds.

g r a ss

h a t

Join the letters to make the words.

g r a b   **d r u m**   **t r i p**

_____   _____   _____

Label the pictures correctly.

_____   _____   _____

Join the letters to make the words and write them below. Draw a picture of the word.

_____   _____   _____

p r a m   **b r i ck**   **c r a sh**

PARENT'S TIPS   Encourage your child to say each sound and 'build up' each word by merging the sounds together.

Colour the **br** leaves brown. Colour the **gr** leaves green.

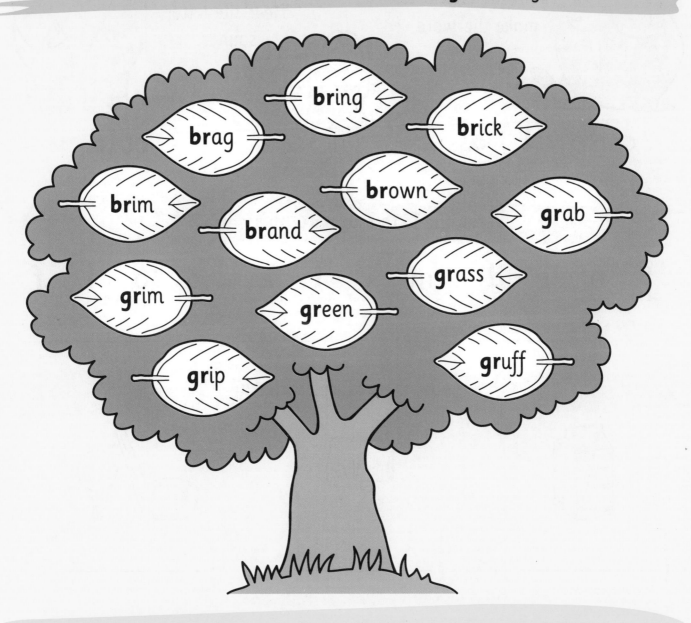

Sort the words in the leaves into sets and write them in the boxes below.

br words

gr words

Join the letters to make the word.

Read the word. Hear the letter sounds.

c o l d

cold

Join the letters to make the words.

f o l d   m i l k   g o l f

_____   _____   _____

Label the pictures correctly.

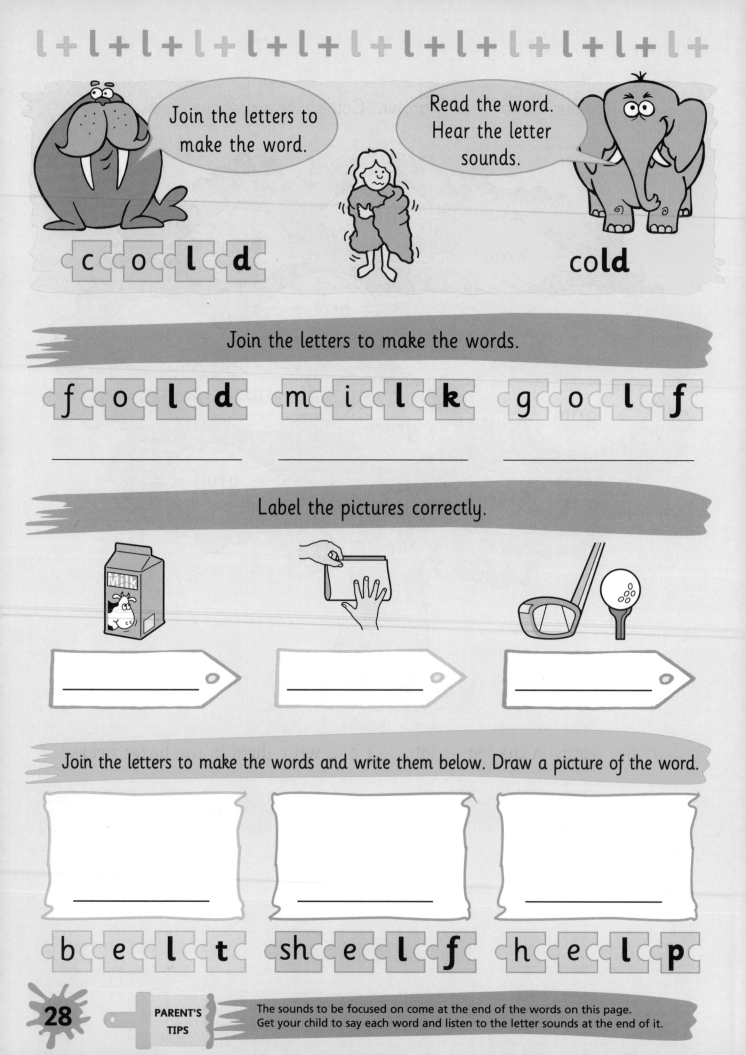

Join the letters to make the words and write them below. Draw a picture of the word.

b e l t   sh e l f   h e l p

PARENT'S TIPS   The sounds to be focused on come at the end of the words on this page. Get your child to say each word and listen to the letter sounds at the end of it.

Build some words ending with **old**.

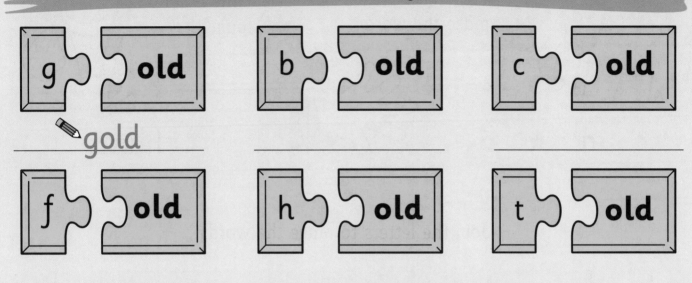

g | old

gold

b | old

c | old

f | old

h | old

t | old

Use the words you built above to answer the crossword clues.

down
1 brave
3 said
5 bend

across
2 not hot
4 metal
6 keep in your hand

PARENT'S TIPS   Use the idea of the jigsaw puzzle pieces to help your child understand how words may be built up and put together.

29

Join the letters to make the word.

Read the word. Hear the letter sounds.

h a **n** d

hand

Join the letters to make the words.

b a **n** d

a **n** t

t a **n** k

_____

_____

_____

Label the pictures correctly.

_____

_____

_____

Join the letters to make the words and write them below. Draw a picture of the word.

_____

_____

_____

p o **n** d

t e **n** t

s i **n** k

PARENT'S TIPS

The sounds to be focused on come at the end of the words on this page. Get your child to say each word and listen to the letter sounds at the end of it.

n + n + n + n + n + n + n + n + n + n + n +

Join up the rhyming words on the two ladders.

Write the words.

Left ladder:
- hand
- bunk
- tent
- pond
- pink
- hunt
- pant
- lend
- bank

Right ladder:
- fond
- punt
- band
- rant
- junk
- send
- went
- sank
- wink

hand   band

PARENT'S TIPS

After joining up the pairs of rhyming words, see how many others you can think of. Make up some rhymes with some of the words e.g. we went in the tent.

31

Build the words and write them below.

ha **nd**	po **nd**	ba **nd**

ba **nk**	si **nk**	wi **nk**

a **nt**	te **nt**	be **nt**

Write each word again under the correct picture.

 bank

  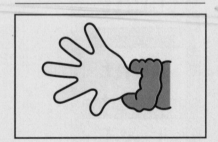

 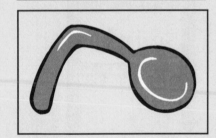 

PARENT'S TIPS Encourage your child to build up and work out the words at the top of the page before matching them to the pictures.